For you.
A beloved child of God.
May you walk with virtue every day of your life!

Virtue is the golden mean between two extremes.
-Aristotle

The Virtuous Path
A Daily Examination of Conscience Journal
for Kids

Welcome!

Many of our greatest stories are about a journey. The hero, and some friends, set out on a quest to accomplish a goal, and they can't get there unless they walk down the path.

The Hobbit, A Whistle for Willie, Hansel and Gretel... these are just a few examples of people heading out into their world and exploring new ideas, learning new skills, and finding out more about themselves.

This book, young adventurer, is for you. It will take you on a four week journey down the Virtuous Path, a path to help you to discover and refine some of the virtues that will help you to become the person God has designed you to be.

Along the way, you will meet some friends to walk along with you, because we are always surrounded by a cloud of witnesses in the Communion of Saints. Take the time to really get to know these partners on your journey and learn all you can from them. You may run into some bumps along the way, and that's OK. Pick yourself up, dust yourself off, and start again.

Our family will be praying for you and your family. Please keep us in your prayers.

+AMDG+
Karianna and Brigid
Pasadena, CA.
August 2020

Also by Karianna Frey:

Serviam Non Serviam: A Daily Examination of Conscience
Available on Amazon.com

A Brief Overview of Diversity
e-book
Available on www.kariannafrey.com

Let's begin the journey!

Each week we will look at our actions and choices through the lens of one the four Cardinal Virtues: Prudence, Justice, Fortitude, and Temperance.

Every night, you will have a chance to think back on your day and reflect on how you lived out the Cardinal Virtues, and how you did not live out the Cardinal Virtues.

You will also have a chance to think about something great that happened to you during your day (your "high") and something not so great that happened during your day (your "low.") You will finish your examination of conscience with a short prayer to God.

On the next page, you will find a description of each of the Cardinal Virtues, as well as some examples of living that virtue out in your life. We've also included an examination of conscience with questions to help guide you along the Virtuous Path.

Finally, you will meet a few Holy men and women in the weekly Saint Spotlights to inspire you and walk with you on the journey, some activities, prayer prompts, and journaling pages to make your own!

Little by little, one travels far.

- An old Spanish saying

What are virtues anyway?

A virtue is another way to describe moral excellence. It's a way of living your life and striving for individual greatness which in turn will help to make the world a better place.

As Catholics, we hold seven virtues close to our hearts: the three theological virtues (Faith, Hope, and Charity) and the four cardinal virtues (Prudence, Justice, Fortitude, and Temperance.) This examination of conscience will help you to look at your day through the lens of the four Cardinal Virtues:

PRUDENCE is the virtue of reason and the act of being careful and choosing the genuine good in every situation.

JUSTICE the virtue of just behavior or treatment. It's the Will of giving God and others the respect that they are due.

TEMPERANCE is the virtue of balance. It keeps us from spending too much time on work and too much time on play.

FORTITUDE is the virtue that gives us strength in difficult situations.

How can I know if I am practicing a Virtue?

Here are some questions that you can ask yourself while doing your examination of conscience. There are, of course, more questions you can ask yourself, but we thought to keep things a little more simple!

Prudence:

- Do I take my time to think before I speak?
- Am I thankful for my daily bread?
- Have I made sure others have what they need?
- Do I give thanks to God in all things?
- Do I spend time in daily prayer with God?
- Do I ask God for help when making decisions?

Justice:

- Do I desire things I do not need?
- Do I treat others as I want to be treated?
- Do I look to correct myself before correcting others?
- Do I look out for others?
- Do I serve others before serving myself?
- Did I obey my parents and others who have authority over me?

Fortitude

- Am I patient with my siblings?
- Do I bear wrongs patiently?
- Do I complain about things?
- Am I willingly carrying my cross?
- Am I able to focus on Jesus during Mass?
- Am I able to endure things… even if they are boring or not fun?

Temperance:

- Do I choose to serve God daily?
- Did I finish what I had to do before doing what I wanted to do?
- Do I try to control my emotions?
- Do I seek to control myself in all situations?
- Am I quick to get angry with others?
- Do I speak with respect to everyone I meet?

"The cardinal virtues are like hinges on which hang all the other moral virtues and our whole moral life. The word "cardinal" is derived from the Latin word "cardo" meaning hinge."

(BC 133)

Virtue demands courage, constant effort, and above all, help from on high.

- St. John Marie Vianney

Week 1:

PRUDENCE

Saint Spotlight

St. Teresa of Avila

St. Teresa of Avila was born Teresa Sánchez de Cepeda y Ahumada in 1515 in Spain. As a child, St. Teresa was fascinated by the lives of the Saints and even ran away from home with her brother so they could try to be martyrs!

After the death of her mother, St. Teresa became devoted to the Blessed Mother and when she was 20, she became a Carmelite nun. During an illness which kept her in bed for almost a year, St. Teresa began to have visions. During these visions, she learned how to better understand mortal and venial sin, the nature of Original Sin, and how important it was to give yourself totally to God.

Many of her friends thought that St. Teresa's visions were not from God. By spending time in prayer and sharing her concerns with her confessor, she was able to see that the visions were from God.

St. Teresa spent a lot of time in prayer and contemplation and did a lot of writing! One of her writings encourages us to have the "ability to know when to proceed and when to retreat, when to take action and when to be still, when to offer help and when to be silent."

St. Teresa of Avila, pray for us!

Kaleb the Ethiopean

Kaleb, also known as St. Elesbaan, was a king of Aksum, an area now known as Ethiopia and Eritrea on the continent of Africa, and is known for ruling his people with wisdom and defending them in battle.

In the 6th Century, Kaleb crossed the Red Sea and invaded the nearby country of Yemen to help the Catholics of that land who were being persecuted and oppressed by Dunaan, a king who was a Catholic and then later left Christianity and started to kill Christians.

After defeating Dunaan, King Kaleb rebuilt the churches that had been destroyed and restored the Faith. Once his mission was complete, Kaleb returned to his country and ruled for many years, instructing his son in the Catholic Faith.

After some time, Kaleb gave up his throne to his son, gave his crown to the Church in Jerusalem, and retired to a monastery to live out his days in prayer and thanksgiving to God.

King Kaleb the Ethiopean, pray for us!

How did each of these Saints show prudence?

_____

_____

_____

_____

_____

Prudence is right reason in action.
- St. Thomas Aquinas

Sunday

Today's Date:

My high for today was

_____

My low for today was

_____

I practiced prudence when I

_____
_____
_____

I did not practice prudence when I

_____
_____
_____

Act of Contrition:
O my God, I am very sorry for all my sins, because
they displease you, who are all good and deserving
of all my love. With your help, I will sin no more.
Amen.

Prudence is right reason in action.
- St. Thomas Aquinas

Monday

Today's Date:

My high for today was

_____

My low for today was

_____

I practiced prudence when I

_____
_____
_____

I did not practice prudence when I

_____
_____
_____

Act of Contrition:
O my God, I am very sorry for all my sins, because
they displease you, who are all good and deserving
of all my love. With your help, I will sin no more.
Amen.

Prudence is right reason in action.
- St. Thomas Aquinas

Tuesday

Today's Date:

My high for today was

_____

My low for today was

_____

I practiced prudence when I

_____

_____

_____

I did not practice prudence when I

_____

_____

_____

Act of Contrition:
O my God, I am very sorry for all my sins, because
they displease you, who are all good and deserving
of all my love. With your help, I will sin no more.
Amen.

Prudence is right reason in action.
- St. Thomas Aquinas

Wednesday

Today's Date:

My high for today was

_____

My low for today was

_____

I practiced prudence when I

_____

_____

_____

I did not practice prudence when I

_____

_____

_____

Act of Contrition:
O my God, I am very sorry for all my sins, because
they displease you, who are all good and deserving
of all my love. With your help, I will sin no more.
Amen.

Prudence is right reason in action.
- St. Thomas Aquinas

Thursday

Today's Date:

My high for today was

_____

My low for today was

_____

I practiced prudence when I

_____

_____

_____

I did not practice prudence when I

_____

_____

_____

Act of Contrition:
O my God, I am very sorry for all my sins, because
they displease you, who are all good and deserving
of all my love. With your help, I will sin no more.
Amen.

Prudence is right reason in action.
- St. Thomas Aquinas

Friday

Today's Date:

My high for today was

_____

My low for today was

_____

I practiced prudence when I

_____

_____

_____

I did not practice prudence when I

_____

_____

_____

Act of Contrition:
O my God, I am very sorry for all my sins, because
they displease you, who are all good and deserving
of all my love. With your help, I will sin no more.
Amen.

Prudence is right reason in action.
- St. Thomas Aquinas

Saturday

Today's Date:

My high for today was

_____

My low for today was

_____

I practiced prudence when I

_____
_____
_____

I did not practice prudence when I

_____
_____
_____

Act of Contrition:
O my God, I am very sorry for all my sins, because
they displease you, who are all good and deserving
of all my love. With your help, I will sin no more.
Amen.

Who am I?

Our names are so important to us because our names tell the world who we are!
With your parents' help, answer the following questions about your name.

1. What is your name?

   _____

2. Does your name mean anything?

   _____

3. Are you named for anyone in particular?

   _____

4. What do you like best about your name?

   _____

5. Why did your parents pick your name for you?

   _____

   _____

   _____

Did you learn something new about your name?
What's even better is that God knew all of this about you before you were even born!

How do I pray the Rosary?

The Rosary is a wonderful devotion! It's like having all of the Gospels in your pocket!

The Rosary is made up of five sets of prayers, each with a specific mystery, (called a decade) during which you are focusing on some part of Jesus' life, often through his Mama, Mary.

We pray different mysteries on different days, and you can find those mysteries, along with all of the prayers, in the Appendix at the back of your book.

Step 1: Holding the crucifix, make the Sign of the Cross.

Step 2: Say the "Apostles Creed" while holding the Crucifix.

Step 3: On the next large bead, say the "Our Father."

Step 4: On the next three small beads, say the "Hail Mary" (one on each bead, one "Hail Mary" for the virtues of Faith, Hope, and Charity.)

Step 5: Say the Glory Be, and the Fatima Prayer.

Step 6: On the next large bead, announce the mystery and pray one "Our Father."

Step 7: On each of the next ten small beads, pray one "Hail Mary."

Step 8: Pray a "Glory Be" and the Fatima Prayer

Step 9: Repeat Steps 6,7, and 8, until you have announced all five mysteries and you are back at the beginning.

Step 10: On the bead or shield that closes the circle on your rosary, pray "Hail Holy Queen" and finish with the "St. Michael Prayer."

Step 11: End with the Sign of the Cross!

The Rosary is such a beautiful way to reflect on all that Jesus has done for us and while it may seem hard in the beginning, you should still give it a try!

Sometimes we like to start our Rosary in the morning and pray the mysteries throughout the day, ending right before dinner! It's a great way to keep Jesus and Mama Mary close to our hearts all day long.

"The Rosary is a prayer that always accompanies me; it is also the prayer of the ordinary people and the Saints... it is a prayer from my heart."

- Pope Francis

Week 2:

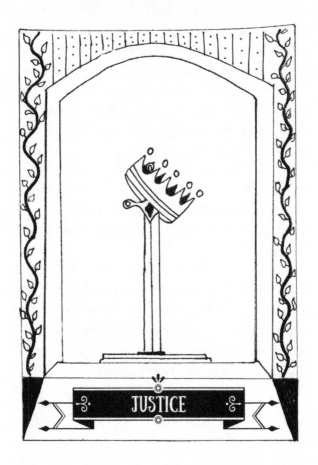

JUSTICE

Saint Spotlight:

St. Katherine Drexel

St. Katherine Drexel was a very wealthy lady who gave up all of her wealth to serve the poor. Katherine grew up helping her family serve others first and started to wonder if God was calling her to become a religious sister!

During a trip out West, Katherine was so upset at how Native Americans were being treated that she wanted the Catholic Church to do something and the Pope told her that SHE was supposed to do something.

So, she left behind everything that she owned (almost $200 million in today's dollars) to help and serve Black and Native Americans, people that many other Americans didn't even think were fully human!

Sadly, many people did not agree with St. Katherine's work and desire that all people should be treated equally, and her order of Sisters had to undergo many hardships, including having a school burned down! St. Katherine did not quit, she kept working for God's justice.

St. Katherine Drexel, pray for us!

St. Martin De Porres

St. Martin De Porres was born in Peru to parents who were not married. His mother was a slave and his father was a Spanish nobleman. Because of St. Martin's mixed-race heritage, people made fun of him and didn't really treat him with respect. He was not even allowed to become a full Religious Brother! The best that he could do is to become a helper to a Religious Order. So St. Martin asked to volunteer with the Dominican Convent of the Rosary and became a servant boy.

St. Martin loved to pray and when he was not working, he was praying, and he especially loved the Blessed Sacrament. Even after he was finally able to become a full Dominincan brother, St. Martin was still made fun of by other priests and friars, even though God performed many miracles through him.

St. Martin is a good example of how we can each do our little bit to make our World a little better every day.

St. Martin de Porres, pray for us!

How were each of these Saints just?

_____

_____

_____

_____

_____

Peace is built on the foundation of justice.
-St. Pope John Paul II

Sunday

Today's Date:

My high for today was

_____

My low for today was

_____

I practiced justice when I

_____

_____

_____

I did not practice justice when I

_____

_____

_____

Act of Contrition:

Dear Jesus, please have mercy on me, a sinner.

Peace is built on the foundation of justice.
-St. Pope John Paul II

Monday

Today's Date:

My high for today was

_____

My low for today was

_____

I practiced justice when I

_____
_____
_____

I did not practice justice when I

_____
_____
_____

Act of Contrition:

Dear Jesus, please have mercy on me, a sinner.

Peace is built on the foundation of justice.
-St. Pope John Paul II

Tuesday

Today's Date:

My high for today was

_____

My low for today was

_____

I practiced justice when I

_____

_____

_____

I did not practice justice when I

_____

_____

_____

Act of Contrition:

Dear Jesus, please have mercy on me, a sinner.

Peace is built on the foundation of justice.
-St. Pope John Paul II

Wednesday

Today's Date:

My high for today was

_____

My low for today was

_____

I practiced justice when I

_____
_____
_____

I did not practice justice when I

_____
_____
_____

Act of Contrition:

Dear Jesus, please have mercy on me, a sinner.

Peace is built on the foundation of justice.
-St. Pope John Paul II

Thursday

Today's Date:

My high for today was

_____

My low for today was

_____

I practiced justice when I

_____
_____
_____

I did not practice justice when I

_____
_____
_____

Act of Contrition:

Dear Jesus, please have mercy on me, a sinner.

Peace is built on the foundation of justice.
-St. Pope John Paul II

Friday

Today's Date:

My high for today was

_____

My low for today was

_____

I practiced justice when I

_____
_____
_____

I did not practice justice when I

_____
_____
_____

Act of Contrition:

Dear Jesus, please have mercy on me, a sinner.

Peace is built on the foundation of justice.
-St. Pope John Paul II

Saturday

Today's Date:

My high for today was

_____

My low for today was

_____

I practiced justice when I

_____

_____

_____

I did not practice justice when I

_____

_____

_____

Act of Contrition:

Dear Jesus, please have mercy on me, a sinner.

Come, Holy Spirit!

Close your eyes and rest in the Holy Spirit for a few minutes. When you feel ready, take some crayons or colored pencils and draw or write what the Holy Spirit inspired you to create!

How do I pray for others?

Praying for others is such a small way to make a big difference in our world. We know that God hears each of our prayers, no matter how long or how short they are.

We can, and should, pray for all of the people around us: our family, our friends, our teachers, the people who help run our cities, states, and country, and we should also pray for the Holy Father and the Bishops!

There is another special group of people that we can pray for, and those are the holy souls in **Purgatory**. Purgatory is where souls go after earthly death to become purified before going to be with Jesus in heaven and we can help the souls in purgatory get to heaven by praying for them and by offering our work (and chores) here on Earth for them.

So the next time you have to do a chore that you really don't want to do, be cheerful and offer that work for a soul in purgatory! You can also pray the "Eternal Rest" prayer:

Eternal rest grant unto them, O Lord, and let perpetual light shine upon them.

May the souls of all the faithful departed, through the mercy of God, rest in peace.

Week 3:

Saint Spotlight:

St. Damien of Molokai

St. Damien of Molokai was born in Belgium and was the youngest of seven children. His father sent him to college to train for a regular profession, but St. Damien was called to the priesthood instead.

When he was 25, Fr. Damien was sent to the Kingdom of Hawai'i to serve the Native Hawaiians who were struggling with diseases which were brought to the islands from foreign traders, sailors, and immigrants.

In 1873, when his brother was too sick to go, Fr. Damien volunteered to travel to a community serve a group of people with leprosy, a disease that we now call "Hanson's Disease." Leprosy is treatable now, but in the 19th Century, people with leprosy could not be treated and often died of the disease.

Despite the risk, Fr. Damien served the lepers, built chapels, roads, hospitals, and churches. He cleaned wounds, dressed residents, shared food and drink, dug graves, and lived with the lepers as equals.

After serving the people of the Kaulaupapa settlement for 16 years, Fr. Damien died from Hanson's Disease in 1889 at the age of 49.

St. Damien of Molokai, pray for us!

Blessed Chiara Bandano

Cancer is no fun for anyone, but, especially when you are a kid.

Blessed Chiara Bandano was born in 1971 and fell in love with Jesus early on in her life. She was often teased in school for her deep faith, but she never stopped loving Jesus.

One day, while she was playing tennis, Bl. Chiara felt a pain in her shoulder, a pain that would turn out to be a painful form of bone cancer. When she found out the news, she simply said, "It's for you Jesus; if you want it, I want it too." Bl. Chiara refused any pain medication during her treatments because she always wanted to know what was going on around her.

Bl. Chiara's faith never failed her, even when she was no longer able to walk and she knew that her death was near. Knowing that her death would allow her to be with Jesus, she faced it with courage and love.

Blessed Chiara Bandano, pray for us!

How did each of these Saints show fortitude?

_____
_____
_____
_____
_____

The Lord is my strength and my song.
- Psalm 118: 14

Sunday

Today's Date:

My high for today was

_____

My low for today was

_____

I practiced fortitude when I

_____

_____

_____

I did not practice fortitude when I

_____

_____

_____

Act of Contrition:

Thank you, Jesus, for today. Please forgive my sins
and help me to be a better disciple tomorrow.

The Lord is my strength and my song.
- Psalm 118: 14

Monday

Today's Date:

My high for today was

_____

My low for today was

_____

I practiced fortitude when I

_____

_____

_____

I did not practice fortitude when I

_____

_____

_____

Act of Contrition:

Thank you, Jesus, for today. Please forgive my sins
and help me to be a better disciple tomorrow.

The Lord is my strength and my song.
- Psalm 118: 14

Tuesday

Today's Date:

My high for today was

_____

My low for today was

_____

I practiced fortitude when I

_____

_____

_____

I did not practice fortitude when I

_____

_____

_____

Act of Contrition:

Thank you, Jesus, for today. Please forgive my sins
and help me to be a better disciple tomorrow.

The Lord is my strength and my song.
- Psalm 118: 14

Wednesday

Today's Date:

My high for today was

_____

My low for today was

_____

I practiced fortitude when I

_____
_____
_____

I did not practice fortitude when I

_____
_____
_____

Act of Contrition:

Thank you, Jesus, for today. Please forgive my sins
and help me to be a better disciple tomorrow.

The Lord is my strength and my song.
- Psalm 118: 14

Thursday

Today's Date:

My high for today was

_____

My low for today was

_____

I practiced fortitude when I

_____
_____
_____

I did not practice fortitude when I

_____
_____
_____

Act of Contrition:

Thank you, Jesus, for today. Please forgive my sins
and help me to be a better disciple tomorrow.

The Lord is my strength and my song.
- Psalm 118: 14

Friday

Today's Date:

My high for today was

_____

My low for today was

_____

I practiced fortitude when I

_____
_____
_____

I did not practice fortitude when I

_____
_____
_____

Act of Contrition:

Thank you, Jesus, for today. Please forgive my sins
and help me to be a better disciple tomorrow.

The Lord is my strength and my song.
- Psalm 118: 14

Saturday

Today's Date:

My high for today was

_____

My low for today was

_____

I practiced fortitude when I

_____

_____

_____

I did not practice fortitude when I

_____

_____

_____

Act of Contrition:

Thank you, Jesus, for today. Please forgive my sins
and help me to be a better disciple tomorrow.

Can you find the words in the puzzle? Look up, down, across, diagonally, and backwards!

```
K A J F L N L N N Y Q E E D E
A N R P O M O R N F K J S C E
T I X A A R O U C Z V Y N C V
H T A R I S T O T L E A I P I
E S Y D A H A I V X R T R E R
R U E R N S C F T E S U J Z T
I A Y R E C K F P U D Q Y W U
N F C R I G L M J E D A I Y E
E H E H M O E T N M V E C O T
J T A N A T T C I S A D O R E
E I L K D P E C I L O H T A C
S J W T T T L W I O B V W A K
U N I T R A M E S V H A B I T
S R R W O U O Q T A K Z P T M
A Y N X S E E G G H B L N E Q
```

VIRTUE
ARISTOTLE
HABIT
PRUDENCE
TERESA
JUSTICE
FORTITUDE
TEMPERANCE
CATHOLIC
ROSARY

JESUS
CHAPLET
KATHERINE
MARTIN
DAMIEN
ISADORE
VICTOIRE
CHIARA
FAUSTINA
MARY

How do I pray the Chaplet of Divine Mercy?

The Chaplet of Divine Mercy was a gift given by Jesus to St. Faustina, a young Polish nun during the 1930s.

St. Faustina was not well educated, so many of her jobs in the convent were simple and humble tasks. However, Jesus visited her often and gave her beautiful messages to share with the world! One of these messages was the Chaplet of Divine Mercy.

During this devotion, we are asking Jesus for his mercy on all of us and on the whole world, even on those people who do not know Jesus yet.

The Chaplet of Divine Mercy is prayed on Rosary Beads, so you can use your Rosary in more ways than one!

Step 1: Holding the Crucifix, make the Sign of the Cross.

Step 2: On the next large bead, pray: "*You expired, Jesus, but the source of life gushed forth for souls, and the ocean of mercy opened up for the whole world. O Fount of Life, unfathomable Divine Mercy, envelop the whole world and empty Yourself out upon us.*"

Then repeat three times: *"O Blood and Water, which gushed forth from the Heart of Jesus as a fount of mercy for us, I trust in You!"*

Step 3: On the next three small beads, pray: one Our Father, one Hail Mary, and one Apostle's Creed

Step 4: On the next large bead pray: *"Eternal Father, I offer you the Body and Blood, Soul and Divinity of Your Dearly Beloved Son, Our Lord, Jesus Christ, in atonement for our sins and those of the whole world."*

Step 5: On the next ten small beads, pray: *"For the sake of His sorrowful Passion, have mercy on us and on the whole world."*

Step 6: Repeat Steps 4 and 5 until you finish all five sets and are back to the beginning of your Rosary.

Step 7: Finish by saying three times: *"Holy God, Holy Mighty One, Holy Immortal One, have mercy on us and on the whole world."*

St. Faustina, pray for us!

Jesus, I Trust In You!

Week 4:

Saint Spotlight:

Blessed Isadore Bakanja

Bl. Isadore Bakanja not only kept his cool, but he even forgave those who hurt him.

Born in 1887, Bl. Isadore was baptized Catholic at the age of 18. He was a gentle young man who loved Mama Mary and carried a Rosary and faithfully wore the Brown Scapular.

Even though he was not an official teacher, Bl. Isadore talked to everyone about Jesus and shared the Good News whenever he could.

Bl. Isadore took a job with a company that did not like the African people or Catholics, and when he asked to be let go from his job, they refused. When Bl. Isadore refused to stop praying or to take off his Brown Scapular, one of the bosses had Bl. Isadore beat so badly that he almost died right there.

While he survived the beating, Bl. Isadore's injuries became infected and he suffered for six more months. Before he died, and while holding his Rosary and wearing his Brown Scapular, Bl. Isadore forgave his attacker, saying: *"Certainly I shall pray for him. When I am in heaven, I shall pray for him very much."*

Blessed Isadore Bakanja, pray for us!

Blessed Victoire Rasoamanarivo

Bl. Victoire was born in 1848 and at age 18, she was baptised Catholic, even though her parents disagreed and threatened to disown her.

Even though she was called to the Religious life, her parents made her marry a man who was very violent toward her. Her friends encouraged her to divorce her husband, but because she knew that marriage was a Sacrament, she refused and prayed for her husband's conversion.

During a time of anti-Catholic feeling in her country, Bl. Victoire continued to live out her Faith in a peaceful manner and even helped others to live in peace until they were free to practice again.

After the conversion, baptism, and death of her husband in 1888, Bl. Victoire lived out the last of her years serving and caring for the poor, the sick, and the imprisoned and devoting herself to prayer.

Blessed Victoire Rasoamanarivo, pray for us!

How did each of these Saints show temperance?

_____

_____

_____

_____

_____

Prayer preserves temperance.
- St. Ephraem

Sunday

Today's Date:

My high for today was

_____

My low for today was

_____

I practiced temperance when I

_____
_____
_____

I did not practice temperance when I

_____
_____
_____

Act of Contrition:

Holy Spirit, Fountain of Love, I call on you with
trust: Purify my heart and help me to walk as a
child of Light.

Prayer preserves temperance.
- St. Ephraem

Monday

Today's Date:

My high for today was

_____

My low for today was

_____

I practiced temperance when I

_____

_____

_____

I did not practice temperance when I

_____

_____

_____

Act of Contrition:

Holy Spirit, Fountain of Love, I call on you with
trust: Purify my heart and help me to walk as a
child of Light.

Prayer preserves temperance.
- St. Ephraem

Tuesday

Today's Date:

My high for today was

_____

My low for today was

_____

I practiced temperance when I

_____
_____
_____

I did not practice temperance when I

_____
_____
_____

Act of Contrition:

Holy Spirit, Fountain of Love, I call on you with
trust: Purify my heart and help me to walk as a
child of Light.

Prayer preserves temperance.
- St. Ephraem

Wednesday

Today's Date:

My high for today was

_____

My low for today was

_____

I practiced temperance when I

_____

_____

_____

I did not practice temperance when I

_____

_____

_____

Act of Contrition:

Holy Spirit, Fountain of Love, I call on you with
trust: Purify my heart and help me to walk as a
child of Light.

Prayer preserves temperance.
- St. Ephraem

Thursday

Today's Date:

My high for today was

_____

My low for today was

_____

I practiced temperance when I

_____

_____

_____

I did not practice temperance when I

_____

_____

_____

Act of Contrition:

Holy Spirit, Fountain of Love, I call on you with
trust: Purify my heart and help me to walk as a
child of Light.

Prayer preserves temperance.
- St. Ephraem

Friday

Today's Date:

My high for today was

_____

My low for today was

_____

I practiced temperance when I

_____

_____

_____

I did not practice temperance when I

_____

_____

_____

Act of Contrition:

Holy Spirit, Fountain of Love, I call on you with
trust: Purify my heart and help me to walk as a
child of Light.

Prayer preserves temperance.
- St. Ephraem

Saturday

Today's Date:

My high for today was

_____

My low for today was

_____

I practiced temperance when I

_____

_____

_____

I did not practice temperance when I

_____

_____

_____

Act of Contrition:

Holy Spirit, Fountain of Love, I call on you with
trust: Purify my heart and help me to walk as a
child of Light.

Counting Your Blessings

We have so much to be grateful for in our lives and
sometimes we forget what God has given to us.
On the lines below, make a list of all of the Blessings in
your life. When you are having a bad, sad, or mad day,
look at your list to remind yourself about the gifts and
people in your life who love you!

_____

_____

_____

_____

_____

_____

_____

_____

_____

_____

_____

_____

_____

_____

_____

_____

How can I pray without ceasing?

Our Faith has a treasure of beautiful prayers, some long and some short, however, you have a wonderful tool for prayer right on the ends of your wrists.

Before he became Pope Francis, Cardinal Bergoglio is said to have written this short prayer that you can pray anytime of the day, using only your fingers!

1. The thumb is the closest finger to you. So start praying for those who are closest to you. They are the easiest people to remember. To pray for our dear ones is a "sweet obligation."

2. The next finger is the index. Pray for those who teach you, instruct you and heal you. They need the support and wisdom to show direction to others. Always keep them in your prayers.

3. The following finger is the tallest. It reminds us of our leaders, the governors and those who have authority. They need God's guidance.

4. The fourth finger is the ring finger. It may surprise you, that it is our weakest finger. It should remind us to pray for the weakest, the sick or those plagued by problems. They need your prayers.

5. And finally we have our smallest finger, the smallest of all. Your pinkie should remind you to pray for yourself. When you are done praying for the other four groups, you will be able to see your own needs but in the proper perspective, and also you will be able to pray for your own needs in a better way.

Congratulations!

You just finished four weeks of daily examinations of conscience, you have walked the Virtuous Path alongside some new Saint friends, and you've learned some new ways to pray!

Take a look back at your weeks and try your best to answer these questions:

Which virtue was the easiest for you to live?

_____

Which virtue was a little more challenging?

_____

Why do you think that virtue was so hard for you?

_____
_____
_____
_____
_____

What can you learn from that hard virtue?

_____
_____
_____
_____

Walking the Virtuous Path takes a lot of effort and it's ok to make mistakes. In fact, making mistakes is how we learn best.

On the next page you can see the steps to receiving the Sacrament of Reconciliation and a page that you can take out of your book and take with you when you go, if you are old enough. If you have not made your first reconciliation yet, that's ok! Having a habit of examining your conscience everyday is a good habit to get into!

In the Sacrament of Reconciliation, you will find Jesus waiting for you (through the priest) and he will forgive your sins and give you advice on how to avoid those sins again. But don't worry if you sin again (because we all do!) Jesus loves you no matter what. The most important thing is to remember to start over and try again!

"Do not be afraid of Confession!"

- Pope Francis

How do I receive the
Sacrament of Reconciliation?

Step 1: After the Priest greets you, make the Sign of the Cross and say, "Bless me, Father, for I have sinned. It has been (say how long) since my last confession. These are my sins." If you don't know how long, you can say "a long time."

Step 2: Tell your sins simply and honestly to Jesus, who acts through the priest. Don't keep anything back. Remember, Jesus loves you.

Step 3: Listen to the advice the priest gives you and remember the penance he tells you to do.

Step 4: Recite an Act of Contrition. This one is one that a lot of people use:

O my God, I am sorry for my sins because I have offended you. I know I should love you above all things. Help me to do penance, to do better, and to avoid anything that might lead me to sin. Amen.

Step 5: The priest will give you absolution and dismiss you. Some will say "Go in Peace" and you can respond "Thanks be to God."

Step 6: Do your penance right away in the church or chapel and be sure to thank God for His mercy!

To be ready for a great confession, look back at your weeks and write down the times when you were not living a virtuous life to give to God in the Sacrament of Reconciliation.

Tear this page out and take with you to confession. Burn, bury, or shred this after receiving absolution and completing your penance.

_____

_____

_____

_____

_____

_____

_____

_____

_____

_____

When you are done, say "For these sins and any that I may have forgotten, I am truly sorry."

After the priest gives you counsel, end with an Act of Contrition

O my God, I am sorry for my sins because I have offended you. I know I should love you above all things. Help me to do penance, to do better, and to avoid anything that might lead me to sin. Amen.

"In failing to confess, Lord, I would only hide You from myself, not myself from You."

-Saint Augustine

Journaling pages

Over the next few pages, you will find some space to journal. Think of journaling like writing a letter to Jesus or using your imagination to be with God. This is your time to put down into words what you are feeling in your heart.

If you need some help starting your journaling, here are some ideas for you!

- God showed me the Garden of Eden, and I saw...
- What do you imagine heaven to be like?
- How can you share the Light of Christ with others?
- Dear Jesus...
- Think of someone from the Bible. What can you learn about him or her?
- Why is it important that we forgive others?
- What gifts or talents has God given to you? How do you use them?
- Think about a Saint that you like. Why do you like them?
- Write a prayer of Thanksgiving to God.
- What Christian song or hymn is your favorite? What makes that song so special to you?
- Do you share your Faith with others? Why or why not?
- How does Jesus show His love for you?

Appendix

Liturgical Calendar, Seasons, and Colors

Did you know that our Church year is broken up into seasons and each of those seasons has a color and theme? See if you can spy these colors in the vestments of the priest and in the wall hangings of your parish.

Advent (purple/rose): This is the beginning of the church year. During the four weeks before Christmas, we are preparing our hearts and minds for the coming of Jesus. On Gaudete Sunday (the 3rd Sunday of Advent) you might see your priest in rose.

Christmas (white): Time to celebrate the birth of Jesus! This season starts on Christmas Eve and continues through the Baptism of Jesus. So, keep those decorations up!

Ordinary Time 1 (green): During Ordinary Time we learn about Jesus' life, teaching, and ministry. Ordinary Time is interrupted by...

Lent (purple/rose/red): This is the time when we enter into the desert for 40 days with Jesus, beginning on Ash Wednesday. It's a time of penance, reflection, and sacrifice to prepare for Easter. On Laetare Sunday (the 4th Sunday of Lent) you might see your priest in rose, while on Palm Sunday, you might see your priest in red.

Paschal Triduum (colors vary): During this very special time, you might see different colors. The Triduum is made up of Holy Thursday, Good Friday, and Holy Saturday.

Easter (white): He is Risen, Alleluia! This is the biggest season of celebration of our Faith and what makes us Christian, the fact that Jesus conquered death! The white vestments and decorations stick around for 50 days!

Pentecost (red): Happy Birthday, Church! On this day we remember God sent the Holy Spirit as tongues of fire on the disciples and and the Church was born!

Ordinary Time 2 (green): This is most of the year for us, where we continue to learn about Jesus and all of his miracles and ministering to all of us as disciples.

Use your crayons or colored pencils to color the year!

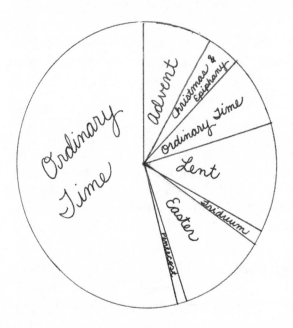

Prayers of the Rosary

Our Father

Our Father, which art in heaven
Hallowed be Thy name.
Thy kingdom come, Thy will be done,
On earth as it is in heaven.
Give us this day our daily bread,
And forgive us our tresspasses
As we forgive those who trespass against us
And lead us not into temptation
But deliver us from evil.
Amen

The Angelic Salutation (Hail Mary)

Hail Mary, full of grace!
The Lord is with thee.
Blessed art thou amongst women
And blessed is the fruit of thy womb, Jesus.
Holy Mary, mother of God,
Pray for us, now, and at the hour of our death.
Amen.

The Gloria Patri

Glory Be to the Father, and to the Son, and to the Holy
Spirit. As it was in the beginning, is now and ever shall
be, world without end. Amen

The Fatima Prayer

Oh My Jesus, forgive us our sins, save us from the fires of hell and lead all souls into heaven, especially those in most need of Your mercy. Amen

Hail, Holy Queen

Hail, Holy Queen, Mother of Mercy,
our life, our sweetness and our hope.
To you do we cry, poor banished children of Eve. To you do we send up our sighs, mourning and weeping in this valley of tears.
Turn then, most gracious advocate, your eyes of mercy toward us, and after this, our exile, show unto us the blessed fruit of thy womb, Jesus.
O clement, O loving, O sweet Virgin Mary.
V/. Pray for us O, Holy Mother of God
R/. That we may be made worthy of the promises of Christ.

Prayer to St. Michael the Archangel

St. Michael the Archangel, defend us in battle,
be our protection against the wickedness
and snares of the devil. May God rebuke him we
humbly pray; and do thou, O Prince of the Heavenly
host, by the power of God, cast into hell Satan
and all the evil spirits who prowl about the world
seeking the ruin of souls.
Amen.

Mysteries of the Rosary:

Joyful: Prayed on Monday and Saturday
    1st: The Annunciation to Mary
    2nd: The Visitation of Mary to Elizabeth
    3rd: The Nativity of Jesus
    4th: The Presentation of Jesus in the Temple
    5th: The Finding of the Child Jesus

Sorrowful: Prayed on Tuesday and Friday
    1st: Christ's Agony in the Garden
    2nd: Christ's scourging at the Pillar
    3rd: Christ is crowned with thorns
    4th: Christ carries his Cross
    5th: Jesus Christ is crucified

Glorious: Prayed on Wednesday and Sunday
    1st: The Resurrection
    2nd: The Ascension of Jesus
    3rd: The Descent of the Holy Spirit at Pentecost
    4th: The Assumption of Mama Mary
    5th: The Coronation (crowning) of Mama Mary

Luminous: Prayed on Thursdays
    1st: The Baptism of Jesus
    2nd: The Wedding Feast at Cana
    3rd: The Proclamation of the Kingdom
    4th: The Transfiguration of Jesus
    5th: The Institution of the Eucharist

Prayers for Every Day

The Guardian Angel Prayer

Angel of God, my guardian dear,
To whom God's love commits me here.
Ever this day* be at my side,
To light, to guard, to rule to guide.
Amen
(* you can say "night" if you say this prayer before bed)

The Morning Offering

O Jesus, through the Immaculate Heart of Mary, I offer
You my prayers, works, joys, and sufferings of this day
for the intentions of Your Sacred Heart, in union with
the Holy Sacrifice of the Mass offered throughout the
world, in reparation for my sins, for the intentions of all
our associates and friends, and for the intentions of the
Holy Father.

Veni Sancte Spiritus

Come, Holy Spirit, fill the hearts of thy faithful
And kindle in them the fire of your love.
Send forth Thy Spirit, and they shall be created.
And Thou shalt renew the face of the earth

The Confiteor

I confess to almighty God, and to you my brothers and
sisters that I have greatly sinned, in my thoughts, and in
my words, in what I have done and in what I have failed
to do Through my fault, through my fault, through my
most grievous fault; therefore I ask blessed Mary, ever
Virgin, all the angels and Saints, and you my brothers
and sisters to pray for me to the Lord our God.

An Act of Faith

O my God, I firmly believe that you are one God in three
divine Persons, Father, Son, and Holy Spirit. I believe
that your divine Son became man and died for our sins
and that he will come to judge the living and the dead. I
believe these and all the truths which the Holy Catholic
Church teaches because You have revealed them who
are eternal truth and wisdom, who can neither deceive
nor be deceived. In this faith I intend to live and die.
Amen.

An Act of Hope

O my God, relying on Your almighty power and infinite
mercy and promises, I hope to obtain pardon of my
sins, the help of Your grace, and life everlasting,
through the merits of Jesus Christ, my Lord and
Redeemer. Amen.

An Act of Love

O my God, I love You above all things, with my whole heart and soul, because you are all-good and worthy of all love. I love my neighbor as myself for the love of You. I forgive all who have injured me, and ask pardon of all whom I have injured. Amen.

The Angelus

Did you know? "V/:" stands for "versicle" and said by the leader while "R/:" stands for "responsorial" and is said by everyone

V/. The Angel of the Lord declared unto Mary,

R/. And she conceived of the Holy Spirit.

Hail Mary...

V/. Behold the handmaid of the Lord,

R/. Be it done unto me according to your Word.

Hail Mary...

V/. And the Word was made flesh,

R/. And dwelt among us.

Hail Mary...

V/. Pray for us, O holy Mother of God,

R/. That we may be made worthy of the promises of Christ.

Let us pray: Pour forth, we beseech you, O Lord, your grace into our hearts: that we, to whom the Incarnation of Christ your Son was made known by the message of an Angel, may by his Passion and Cross be brought to the glory of his Resurrection. Through the same Christ our Lord. Amen.

The Regina Coeli
(said during Eastertide instead of the Angelus)

Queen of Heaven, rejoice, Alleluia!
For He Whom you did deserve to bear, Alleluia!
Has risen as He said, Alleluia!
Pray for us to God, Alleluia!
V/. Rejoice and Be glad, O Virgin Mary! Alleluia!
R/. Because our Lord is truly risen, Alleluia!

Let us pray. O God, Who by the Resurrection of Your
Son, Our Lord Jesus Christ, has vouchsafed to make
glad the whole world, grant, we beseech You, that
through the intercession of the Virgin Mary, His
Mother, we may attain the joys of eternal life. Through
the same Christ Our Lord. Amen

The Generosity Prayer
By St. Ignatius of Loyola

Lord, teach me to be generous.
Teach me to serve You as You deserve.
To give, and not to count the cost,
To fight, and not to heed the wounds,
To toil, and not to seek for rest,
To labor, and not to ask for reward,
Save that knowing that I am doing your will through
Christ, our Lord.
Amen.

Acknowledgements

Thank you to Lina Martin for encouraging this idea and to Kat Landa for being a second set of eyes! This book is really only here because of them.

A huge thanks goes to my loving husband, Steve, who was happy to wrangle the preschooler long enough for me to get an idea jotted down.

Of course, all glory and honor goes to my Lord and Savior, and best friend forever, Jesus, and his beautiful Mother, Mary. Thank you for loving me.

- Karianna

Thank you to my art teachers at SMA for encouraging me to sketch my world around me!

Thank you to my BFF, Liana Cross, for the beautiful sketch book that became the canvas for all of the images in this book.

And, of course, thank you to my mama and daddy and thank you to God for giving me all of my talents.

- Brigid

About the Author

Karianna converted to Catholicism in 2001 and is a lover of the Sacraments, especially the Sacrament of Reconciliation. A graduate of the University of Wisconsin-Madison, Karianna lives in Southern California with her husband and four children.

About the Illustrator

Brigid is a cradle Catholic and loves to read, draw, and play the viola. Her happy place is the beach where you can find her jumping in the waves. She is the oldest of four children and absolutely loves Legos.

Made in the USA
Monee, IL
05 June 2021

70302808R00059